SCHOLASTIC

SATs Made Simple

Maths Problem Solving & Reasoning

Ages 10–11

Explain ÷ Strategy Method £

Measures Time + Operations

Record

Solution Pattern

Area 🕐 Sequence

Data Money ✕

– Problem

Statistics

SCHOLASTIC

Published in the UK by Scholastic Education, 2021
Book End, Range Road, Witney, Oxfordshire, OX29 0YD
A division of Scholastic Limited
London – New York – Toronto – Sydney – Auckland
Mexico City – New Delhi – Hong Kong

SCHOLASTIC and associated logos are trademarks and/or
registered trademarks of Scholastic Inc.
www.scholastic.co.uk

© 2021 Scholastic Limited

1 2 3 4 5 6 7 8 9   1 2 3 4 5 6 7 8 9 0

A British Library Cataloguing-in-Publication Data
A catalogue record for this book is available from the
British Library.

ISBN 978-1407-18402-9
Printed and bound by Ashford Colour Press

Papers used by Scholastic Limited are made from wood grown in
sustainable forests.

Author
Paul Hollin

Editorial team
Robin Hunt, Rachel Morgan, Kate Baxter, Tracy Kewley,
David and Jackie Link, Suzanne Holloway

Design team
Dipa Mistry, QBS Learning

Illustration
QBS Learning

Contents

How to use this book 4

Progress chart 5

1 Question type 1: choosing options and filling in blanks 6

2 Question type 2: thinking things through and giving explanations 8

3 Question type 3: solving problems 10

4 Place value and rounding 12

5 Addition and subtraction 14

6 Multiplication and division 16

7 Order of operations 18

8 Fractions: identifying, simplifying and comparing 20

9 Fractions: adding, subtracting, multiplying and dividing 22

10 Fractions, decimals and percentages 24

11 Decimals and money 26

12 Ratio and proportion 28

13 Patterns, sequences and algebra 30

14 Measurement: perimeter, area and volume 32

15 Measurement: length, mass and capacity 34

16 Geometry: angles and shapes 36

17 Geometry: position, direction and coordinates 38

18 Time, distance and speed 40

19 Data handling: simple charts 42

20 Data handling: graphs, pie charts and statistics 44

Practice test 46

The answers can be found online at: **www.scholastic.co.uk/sats-problem-solving**

How to use this book

This book provides you with a step-by-step guide to all aspects of solving mathematical problems, providing a complete route to mastery of this essential area of the National Curriculum for mathematics for older primary-age children.

In the Key Stage 2 mathematics tests there is one Arithmetic paper and two Reasoning papers. The Reasoning papers involve solving problems, and thinking about and explaining how to solve the problems. This is reasoning in mathematics. The reasoning papers make up 60 per cent of the total mark in the Key Stage 2 SATs.

In this book, there are 20 units and a practice test.

In Units 1–3, you will learn about the different question types that are found in the SATs reasoning papers.

Units 4–20 have this format:

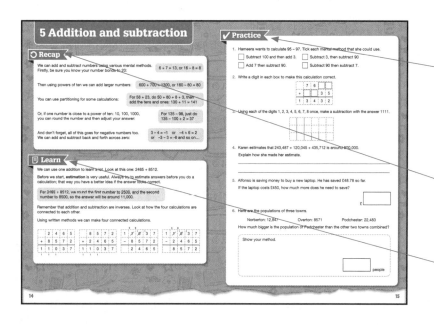

Practice – practise what you have learned by solving problems similar to the ones found in the SATs tests. For each unit, these start easy and get harder.

Recap – review what you should have learned already.

Learn – facts and skills you need to tackle the questions.

Try Units 1, 2 and 3 first. As well as introducing you to the different problem-solving question types, these units include tips for how best to solve each one. At the end of the book is an assessment test to see how well you can answer questions for different topics.

A handy progress chart on page 5 allows you to track your understanding. It is a good idea to tick off a section only when all of the questions have been completed correctly, with mistakes corrected and any misunderstandings clarified.

All answers can be found online at **www.scholastic.co.uk/sats-problem-solving**

Progress chart

Making progress? Tick (✔) the circles as you complete each unit of the book.

Work through one unit at a time before moving on to the next one.

1 Question type 1: choosing options and filling-in blanks

2 Question type 2: thinking things through and giving explanations

3 Question type 3: solving problems

4 Place value and rounding

5 Addition and subtraction

6 Multiplication and division

7 Order of operations

8 Fractions: identifying, simplifying and comparing

9 Fractions: adding, subtracting, multiplying and dividing

10 Fractions, decimals and percentages

11 Decimals and money

12 Ratio and proportion

13 Patterns, sequences and algebra

14 Measurement: perimeter, area and volume

15 Measurement: length, mass and capacity

16 Geometry: angles and shapes

17 Geometry: position, direction and coordinates

18 Time, distance and speed

19 Data handling: simple charts

20 Data handling: graphs, pie charts and statistics

Well done!

1 Question type 1: choosing options and filling in blanks

Working through this unit, you will be introduced to two straightforward types of Reasoning questions that you may have to solve in the SATs tests.

Choosing options

These types of questions are usually worth one mark. Sometimes you have to choose one option, sometimes more than one. You don't have to show any working out, but you can still write things down if it helps you to decide the answer. These questions should only take a minute or so to answer.

1. Tick the decimal that equals $\frac{3}{4}$.

> This is a multiple-choice question, with one correct answer to choose.

Remember: divide the numerator (top number) by the denominator (bottom number) to convert a fraction to a decimal.

0.8	0.57	0.75	0.34	0.43
☐	☐	☐	☐	☐

2. Circle all the acute angles.

> This is a multiple-choice question that may have more than one correct choice.

Remember: an acute angle is less than 90°.

3. The pie chart on page 7 shows 12 children's choices for lunch. Tick each statement that is true.

> This is a 'True or false' question – a kind of multiple choice, often with more than one answer to be ticked.

Remember: a pie chart is 360° and each section is a proportion of that.

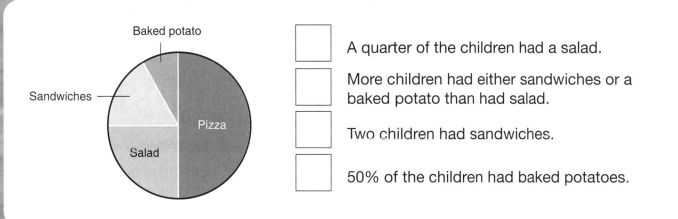

A quarter of the children had a salad.

More children had either sandwiches or a baked potato than had salad.

Two children had sandwiches.

50% of the children had baked potatoes.

Fill in the blanks – write numbers in the spaces

With one or more blank spaces in which to write a number, these questions should also only take a minute or so to answer.

1. Write the **same digit** in each space to complete this calculation.

You need to complete a calculation.

> **Remember:** BIDMAS – multiplication comes before addition.

$\boxed{} + 6 \times \boxed{} = 14$

2. Write the missing number in this sequence.

In this question, you need to work out the rule and write the next numbers.

> Try looking at the difference between each number.

12	25	51	103	

3. Write the missing digits to make this subtraction correct.

Think about written methods to complete the calculation.

> **Remember:** use exchanging (borrowing) for subtraction.

	2	4	7	☐
−	1	☐	3	5
		7	3	8

2 Question type 2: thinking things through and giving explanations

Working through this unit, you will be introduced to two types of Reasoning questions that require you to think carefully about **what** is being asked and **how** you will work out your answer. These questions should take you a couple of minutes to answer.

Thinking things through

These questions don't usually ask you to find an answer to a calculation or to solve a problem. Instead, you have to use information to create an answer, and there may be more than one possible answer.

> The best approach is to think carefully about what you are being asked to do, and what mathematics skills and knowledge you need to use.

1. Arrange these cards to make the largest number possible.

   | 4 | 1 | 8 | 3 |

2. Tim does an addition calculation in his book.
   He says, "1707 + 875 = 2582."

   Do a subtraction to check if he is right.

3. Josie goes to the fruit shop with £8. She has to buy **at least** four of each type of fruit, and have less than 20p change.

   Write one solution to show what can she buy.

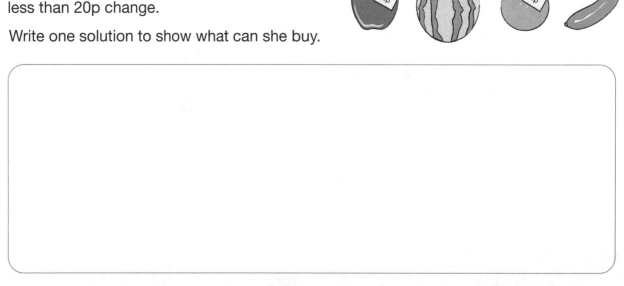

Giving explanations

These questions require you to show that you understand a calculation, or why a mistake has been made. You will need to use words (and sometimes numbers) to explain why a mathematical calculation or idea is correct or incorrect. These questions should also take you a couple of minutes to answer.

> The best approach is to study the question carefully, and write down the calculation if it is shown in words.

1. A 2D shape has four identical sides. Adam says it must be a square.

   Explain why he is wrong.

   > Identify the mistake and explain it.   Think about quadrilateral facts.

   _____

   _____

   _____

2. Jill says that 0.45 is bigger than $\frac{2}{5}$.

   Explain why she is correct.

   > Identify the calculation involved. You can then include it in your explanation if you wish, but you don't have to.   Think about fractions as decimals.

   _____

   _____

   _____

3. Ahmed wants to calculate 300×21. Explain a mental method he could use.

   > Identify the maths involved.

   _____

   _____

   _____

3 Question type 3: solving problems

You will have to solve several problems in the two Reasoning SATs papers. Sometimes these are worth two marks, and you may be asked to show your method.

Single-step problems

These types of questions are usually examples of real-life maths, with one calculation to complete. They vary in difficulty.

> These questions often involve units, such as centimetres or seconds, that have to be converted. Make sure you get the units right!

> Always try to estimate the answer before you start. This will tell you if what you calculate looks right.

1. One quarter of all cars passing a school's gates are white. If 120 cars drive past in an hour, how many will be white?

   ⬜ cars

2. If 200 people each pay £9.50 to watch a film, how much will be collected altogether?

   > Sometimes a mental method is quicker than a written method.

   £ ⬜

3. A barrel is filled to the top with 84 litres of water. A hole in the bottom of the barrel lets out 12ml per minute.

   How long will it take the tank to empty?

   > Think about powers of ten and your times tables facts.

   Remember: 1 litre = 1000 millilitres.

   ⬜ minutes

Multi-step problems (show your method)

There are often a few of these questions in each SATs test. They are sometimes tricky and take longer to answer. They have more than one calculation, and you usually have to show your working out, or 'method'.

Don't start working until you have a plan. Think it through and, if possible, estimate your answer before you start.

1. Jane has £50. She buys eight books for £5.50 each, and then sells two of them for £8 each.

   How much money will she have now?

   Show your method.

   £ [   ]

2. There are 24,000 people watching a football match. Two-thirds of them support the red team, and one-quarter of the red team supporters are children.

   How many children support the red team?

   Show your method.

   [   ] children

3. A builder uses large and small bricks. One large brick and one small brick weigh 550 grams. Three large bricks and a small brick weigh 1.35 kilograms.

   Find the weight of a large brick.

   Show your method.

   [   ] grams

4 Place value and rounding

Our number system is called base 10. It uses the digits 0 to 9 to represent different powers of ten such as ones, tens, hundreds and thousands.

For example, we can write the number two thousand five hundred and eighty-three like this:

Thousands	Hundreds	Tens	Ones
2	5	8	3

📄 Learn

What is 1000 more than 2583?

It's 3583. Just add 1 to the thousands column.

What's the biggest number you can make with the digits 4, 1, 6 and 3?

It's 6431. Just arrange the digits from largest to smallest.

Round 2583 to different powers of ten.

2583 to the nearest ten is 2580, to the nearest hundred is 2600, to the nearest thousand is 3000.

Can you explain the rule?

If the digit to the next-lowest power of ten is 5 or more, round up. If not, round down.

Now try with a bigger number. What is 50,000 more than 3,520,419?

It's 3,570,419. Just add 5 to the ten thousands column.

What's the biggest number you can make with the digits 3, 5, 2, 0, 4, 1, 9?

It's 9,543,210. Just arrange the digits from largest to smallest.

Round 3,520,419 to the nearest thousand, hundred thousand and million.

3,520,419 to the nearest thousand is 3,520,000; to the nearest hundred thousand is 3,500,000; to the nearest million is 4,000,000.

1. What is the second-largest number you can make by rearranging these four cards? Write the number in the box.

    | 5 | 5 | 8 | 6 |

    [   ]

2. Round 245,063.

To the nearest hundred	To the nearest thousand	To the nearest ten thousand

3. Draw a circle around the smallest number:

    1,092,482   1,029,482   1,209,482   1,290,482

4. Complete this chart. Write the missing numbers.

100 less	Number	1000 more
7730	7830	8830
	2110	
		1825
45		

5. Jim estimates the addition 12,479 + 6512.

    He rounds each number to the nearest thousand and says his answer is 18,000.

    Explain where Jim has gone wrong, and what his answer should be.

    _____

    _____

6. A large city has an estimated population of 12,487,000.

    If the population of the city grows by 10,000 people every year, what will be the population in five years' time?

    [   ] people

5 Addition and subtraction

↻ Recap

We can add and subtract numbers using various mental methods. Firstly, be sure you know your number bonds to 20:

$6 + 7 = 13$, or $16 - 8 = 8$

Then using powers of ten we can add larger numbers:

$600 + 700 = 1300$, or $160 - 80 = 80$

You can use partitioning for some calculations:

For $58 + 23$, do $50 + 80 + 8 + 3$, then add the tens and ones: $130 + 11 = 141$

Or, if one number is close to a power of ten: 10, 100, 1000, you can round the number and then adjust your answer:

For $135 - 98$, just do $135 - 100 + 2 = 37$

And don't forget, all of this goes for negative numbers too. We can add and subtract back and forth across zero:

$3 - 4 = -1$ or $-4 + 6 = 2$ or $-3 - 3 = -6$ and so on...

📄 Learn

We can use one addition to learn a lot. Look at this one: $2465 + 8512$.

Before we start, **estimation** is very useful. Always try to estimate answers before you do a calculation; that way you have a better idea if the answer looks correct.

For $2465 + 8512$, we round the first number to 2500, and the second number to 8500, so the answer will be around 11,000.

Remember that addition and subtraction are inverses. Look at how the four calculations are connected to each other.

Using written methods we can make four connected calculations.

	2	4	6	5
+	8	5	7	2
1	1	0	3	7
	1	1	1	

	8	5	7	2
+	2	4	6	5
1	1	0	3	7
	1	1	1	

1	¹⁄1	¹0	¹3	7
−	8	5	7	2
	2	4	6	5

1	¹⁄1	¹0	¹3	7
−	2	4	6	5
	8	5	7	2

1. Hameera wants to calculate 95 – 97. Tick each mental method that she could use.

   ☐ Subtract 100 and then add 3.   ☐ Subtract 3, then subtract 90

   ☐ Add 7 then subtract 90.   ☐ Subtract 90 then subtract 7.

2. Write a digit in each box to make this calculation correct.

		7	6		
+				3	5
1	3	4	3	2	

3. Using each of the digits 1, 2, 3, 4, 5, 6, 7, 8 once, make a subtraction with the answer 1111.

4. Karen estimates that 243,487 + 120,045 + 435,712 is around 800,000.

   Explain how she made her estimate.

   _____

   _____

5. Alfonso is saving money to buy a new laptop. He has saved £48.78 so far.

   If the laptop costs £450, how much more does he need to save?

   £ ☐

6. Here are the populations of three towns.

   Norberton: 12,847   Overton: 8571   Podchester: 22,483

   How much bigger is the population of Podchester than the other two towns combined?

   Show your method.

   ☐ people

6 Multiplication and division

Multiplication and division facts are always popular in the SATs test, especially as part of multi-step problems.

↻ Recap

Multiplication is repeated addition:

$6 + 6 + 6 = 18$, so $3 \times 6 = 18$

Division is repeated subtraction.

$18 - 6 - 6 - 6 = 0$, so $18 \div 3 = 6$

You need to know your times tables. They give us lots of number facts. Multiplication can be done in any order:

$3 \times 4 = 12$ and $4 \times 3 = 12$

Multiplication and division are **inverses**:

$5 \times 7 = 35$ and $35 \div 7 = 5$

Square numbers are special:

$3 \times 3 = 9$, $8 \times 8 = 64$, $11 \times 11 = 121$

Prime numbers are special too:

A prime number can only be divided by itself and 1.

Factors are the numbers that divide into another number.

1, 2, 4 and 8 are all factors of 8.

Multiples are made by multiplying one number by another.

10 is a multiple of 1, 2, 5 and 10.

📄 Learn

Remember, you can quickly multiply and divide numbers by powers of 10.

$34 \times 10{,}000 = 340{,}000$

$27 \div 1000 = 0.027$

Make sure you understand how to use written methods to solve long multiplication and long division. Be careful carrying the right numbers and remainders forward.

85×23

Estimate:
$90 \times 20 = 1800$

			8	5
			2	3
		2	5¹	5
+	1	7¹	0	0
	1	9	5	5

$126 \div 8$

Estimate:
$126 \div 10 = 12.6$

$$8 \overline{)1^12^46}\quad 15\,r\,6$$

$$8 \overline{)1^12^46.^60^40}\quad 15.75$$

1. Circle the number that is ten times greater than three hundred and five.

   3500   3005   305   3050   350

2. Complete the grid.

	8	12	20	100	800
× 5	40				
÷ 4	2				

3. Kavi says, "If 12 × 12 is 144, then 144 ÷ 24 must be 6." Explain how she knows.

   _____

   _____

4. Tina thinks of a number. She says it is a multiple of two, and one of its factors is six. The numbers one less and one more than it are both prime numbers.

   Which are the lowest two numbers she could be thinking of?   ☐ and ☐

5. A library has 2500 books. The books need to be put onto new shelves that hold exactly 80 books each. Once all the shelves are full, any leftover books are sold for £4.50 each.

   How much money is made by selling the leftover books?

   Show your method.

   £ ☐

6. A gardener says that for every eight carrot seeds planted, only five carrots grow. If he grows 70 carrots, how many seeds did he plant?

   ☐ seeds

7 Order of operations

↻ Recap

A maths operation is single calculation, such as divide, square or subtract.

When we have a calculation with several operations we call it multi-step.

So, 4 + 5 – 3 is a multi-step calculation. And for addition and subtraction it doesn't matter if we do the + or the – first.

> Doing the + first, 4 + 5 – 3 = 9 – 3, and 9 – 3 = 6

> Doing the – first, 4 + 5 – 3 = 4 + 2, and 4 + 2 = 6

Multi-step calculations using other operations, like multiplication, have a set of rules you must follow.

📄 Learn

The rule for all multi-step calculations is **BIDMAS**. It tells us the order to do the operations in complex calculations: **B** first to **S** last. BIDMAS stands for:

Brackets   Indices   Division   Multiplication   Addition   Subtraction

So, if any part of a calculation is in brackets, that part must be done first.

> And remember, indices means powers – squared or cubed, e.g. $3^2 = 9$

Start with an easy calculation: 4 + 3 × 2

> Multiplication comes before addition, so we will have 4 + 6, which equals 10.

But if we had included brackets: (4 + 3) × 2

> Brackets come before multiplication, so we will have 7 × 2, which equals 14.

Or, now try it with indices: 4^2 + 3 × 2

> Indices come before multiplication, so we will have 16 + 3 × 2, which equals 22.

Let's include some brackets around the indices: (4^2 + 3) × 2

> Brackets first, giving us 19. Next come multiplication, 19 × 2 = 38

1. Write the missing numbers in the boxes.

$12 \div 4 - 3 = \boxed{}$ $9 - 2 \times 3 + \boxed{} = 8$

2. Insert the missing bracket to make the calculation correct.

$6 \times 2 + 5 - 4) = 18$

3. Use each of these digits and symbols once to make a correct calculation.

2   3   4   5   ×   −   +

       $= 9$

4. Molly does a calculation: $(1 + 2^2) \times 2 - 4 \div 2 = 3$

Explain her mistake.

_____

_____

5. Oliver buys two pens and a ruler.

How much change will he receive from a £10 note?

£2.60

£1.50

£ $\boxed{}$

6. Beth is having a party. She buys three small packs of balloons and two large packs. Small packs have 15 balloons each, and large packs have 25 balloons each.

If 17 of the balloons burst when they are being blown up, how many balloons will there be for the party?

Show your method.

$\boxed{}$ balloons

8 Fractions: identifying, simplifying and comparing

↻ Recap

A fraction is a proportion of one whole.

We can show fractions with diagrams, or write them using numbers.

$$\frac{1}{2}$$

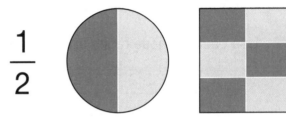

> One half or one over two means one out of two. When we use numbers the **numerator** is on the top, and the **denominator** is on the bottom.

The denominator tells us the total number of parts, and the numerator tells us how many of the parts are in the fraction.

📄 Learn

Fractions can be simplified. This shape has two out of eight squares shaded.

The shape also has one out of every four squares shaded,

so $\frac{2}{8} = \frac{1}{4}$.

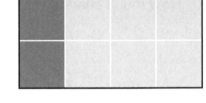

We can say $\frac{2}{8} = \frac{1 \times 2}{4 \times 2}$

then 'cancel out' the × 2 on the top and bottom.

> So $\frac{2}{8} = \frac{1}{4}$ are **equivalent fractions**.

To compare fractions, we need to give them a **common denominator**.

Which is bigger, $\frac{5}{6}$ or $\frac{3}{4}$?

We can use the lowest common denominator – the number that 6 and 4 both go into. Using times tables facts, we know that it is 12.

> Remember, to make an equivalent fraction we multiply the numerator AND the denominator by the same number.

So, we convert each fraction into twelfths: $\frac{2 \times 5}{2 \times 6} = \frac{10}{12}$ $\qquad$ $\frac{3 \times 3}{3 \times 4} = \frac{9}{12}$

> So $\frac{5}{6}$ is bigger. We say $\frac{5}{6} > \frac{3}{4}$

1. Tick the shapes which have $\frac{1}{4}$ shaded.

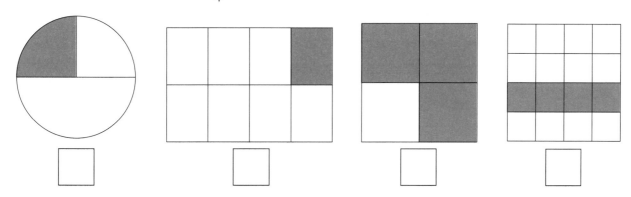

☐   ☐   ☐   ☐

2. Draw lines to connect each pair of equivalent fractions

| $\frac{1}{2}$ | $\frac{1}{8}$ | $\frac{1}{4}$ | $\frac{1}{6}$ | $\frac{1}{3}$ |

| $\frac{6}{24}$ | $\frac{4}{24}$ | $\frac{12}{24}$ | $\frac{3}{24}$ | $\frac{8}{24}$ |

3. Write the **same digit** in each box, so that each number sentence is true.

$$\frac{1}{3} > \frac{\Box}{8} \qquad \frac{1}{3} < \frac{\Box}{5}$$

4. Jamal says, "$\frac{15}{40}$ is equivalent to $\frac{3}{8}$". Explain why he is correct.

_____

_____

5. Circle the smallest fraction in each pair.

$3\frac{2}{5}$ $\frac{16}{5}$ $\frac{39}{8}$ $5\frac{1}{8}$

$\frac{30}{4}$ $7\frac{3}{8}$ $\frac{35}{42}$ $\frac{63}{84}$

9 Fractions: adding, subtracting, multiplying and dividing

We can only add and subtract two fractions if they have the same denominator.

So $\frac{1}{2} + \frac{1}{4}$ becomes $\frac{2}{4} + \frac{1}{4} = \frac{3}{4}$

> We find the lowest common denominator: 2 and 4 are both factors of 4. So we change $\frac{1}{2}$ into $\frac{2}{4}$ by multiplying the top and bottom by 2.

What about subtraction? How would we calculate $\frac{1}{2} - \frac{1}{3}$?

> The lowest common denominator is 6 so we change both fractions into sixths: change $\frac{1}{2}$ into $\frac{3}{6}$ by multiplying the top and bottom by 3; change $\frac{1}{3}$ into $\frac{2}{6}$ by multiplying the top and bottom by 2.

$\frac{3}{6} - \frac{2}{6} = \frac{1}{6}$

📄 Learn

To multiply and divide two fractions, the fractions don't need the same denominator.

$\frac{2}{3} \times \frac{6}{7} = \frac{12}{21} = \frac{4}{7}$

> Numerator × numerator, denominator × denominator, then simplify.

Whole numbers can be multiplied by fractions:

$\frac{1}{4} \times 3 = \frac{1}{4} \times \frac{3}{1} = \frac{3}{4}$

$\frac{3}{4} \times 2 = \frac{3}{4} \times \frac{2}{1} = \frac{6}{4} = \frac{3}{2}$ (or $1\frac{1}{2}$)

> **Remember:** a whole number has a denominator of 1. Usually we don't write it, but it's always there.

For $\frac{1}{2} \times 3\frac{1}{3}$ change $3\frac{1}{3}$ to $10\frac{1}{3}$ then multiply by $\frac{1}{2}$.

To divide a fraction by a fraction, remember **keep**, **change**, **flip** – we **keep** the first fraction, **change** the sign, then **flip** the second fraction.

Look at these examples: $\frac{1}{2} \div \frac{3}{5} = \frac{1}{2} \times \frac{5}{3} = \frac{5}{6}$ $\frac{1}{3} \div 4 = \frac{1}{3} \times \frac{1}{4} = \frac{1}{12}$

> Can you see the flipped fractions?

1. Here are two calculations. Write the missing digit so that both the answers are the same.

   $\frac{1}{2} + \frac{2}{6}$

   $1 - \dfrac{\boxed{}}{6}$

2. One third of Class 6's art colouring pencils need sharpening.

   If they have 72 pencils altogether, how many need sharpening?

    pencils

3. Circle every calculation that is correct.

   $\frac{2}{3} \times \frac{5}{7} = \frac{10}{21}$ $\frac{1}{3} \times \frac{3}{8} = \frac{1}{8}$ $\frac{5}{7} \times \frac{3}{4} = \frac{1}{2}$ $12 \times \frac{3}{4} = 9$

4. A pizza is cut into eight equal slices. If Joanne has a quarter of the pizza and her sister has three slices, what fraction of the pizza is left over?

5. Amina says, "One half divided by one quarter equals two."

   Explain why she is right.

   _____

   _____

6. In a school, half of the children are girls, and two-thirds of the girls have blue eyes.

   If there are 282 children in the school, how many of the girls have blue eyes?

   Show your method.

    girls

10 Fractions, decimals and percentages

Fractions, decimals and percentages all represent a **proportion** of a whole.

A fraction has a number of equal parts, such as 1 out of 4 or $\frac{1}{4}$.

A decimal uses tenths, hundredths and thousandths, such as 0.253.

A percentage is always out of 100, which represents a whole. So 75 out of 100 is 75%.

The three always have **equivalences** to each other. Look at these examples.

Fraction	$\frac{1}{10}$	$\frac{1}{4}$	$\frac{1}{2}$	$\frac{5}{8}$	$\frac{5}{5}$
Decimal	0.1	0.25	0.5	0.625	1.0
Percentage	10%	25%	50%	62.5%	100%

📝 Learn

To convert a fraction to a decimal, the numerator (the number on the top) is divided by the denominator (the number on the bottom).

$$\frac{1}{2} = 1 \div 2 = 0.5 \qquad \frac{3}{5} = 3 \div 5 = 0.6$$

Division with decimals is the same as dividing with whole numbers.

For 3 ÷ 5, we say 5 won't go into 3, so carry the 3 over the decimal point.
5 into 30 goes 6, so 3 ÷ 5 = 0.6

$$\begin{array}{r} 0.6 \\ 5 \overline{)3.^30} \end{array}$$

To convert a fraction to a percentage, make an equivalent fraction with a denominator of 100.

$$\frac{1}{2} = \frac{50}{100} \text{ or } 50\% \qquad \frac{1}{4} = \frac{25}{100} \text{ or } 25\%$$

To convert a decimal to a percentage, just multiply by 100. For example 0.37 × 100 = 37%.

To find a percentage of a number, change to a fraction or decimal and calculate.

$$45\% \text{ of } 320 = \frac{45}{100} \times 320 \text{ or } 0.45 \times 320$$

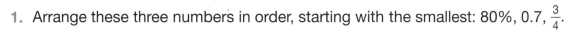

Practice

1. Arrange these three numbers in order, starting with the smallest: 80%, 0.7, $\frac{3}{4}$.

☐ ☐ ☐

2. Complete the chart.

Fraction	$\frac{1}{4}$			
Decimal		0.4		
Percentage			75%	90%

3. Insert any of these symbols into these two statements to make them true.

< > =

$\frac{3}{8}$ ☐ 40% 0.65 ☐ $\frac{3}{5}$

4. 36% of pets in the UK are dogs. What fraction of pets in the UK are not dogs? Please give your answer in its simplest form.

5. 40% of people at a football match are children. Ahmed says that if there are 800 people at the match, there must be 320 children. Explain how he found his answer.

_____

_____

6.

Filling	Cheese	Salad	Hummus	Egg	Total
Children	7	6	5	7	25

Josie and Beth did a class survey of favourite sandwich fillings. What percentage of children did **not** choose cheese as their favourite filling?

Show your method.

☐ %

11 Decimals and money

↻ Recap

Decimals are used to show a part of one whole.

Ones	.	Tenths	Hundredths	Thousandths
3	.	7	2	5

We say three point seven two five.

> Hundredths are smaller than tenths, and thousandths are even smaller. Imagine a huge cake cut into 1000 equal slices; each one would be one-thousandth of the whole.

Money is often written as decimals, because each pound can be divided into 100 pence.

> £2.99 is two £1 coins, nine 10p coins and nine 1p coins (or 99p).

Remember, there are no thousandths with money.

📄 Learn

We add and subtract decimals in the same way as we add and subtract whole numbers, using our base 10 system – hundreds, tens, ones, tenths, hundredths and thousandths.

$3.26 + 5.41 = 8.67$ $0.452 + 0.29 = 0.742$ $2.42 + 1.85 = 4.27$

$1 - 0.43 = 0.57$ $0.637 - 0.4 = 0.237$ $3.57 - 1.5 = 2.07$

> Notice how the tenths are added to tenths and so on, and numbers are exchanged (borrowed), just like in regular addition and subtraction.

We multiply and divide decimals by whole numbers in the same way as we do with whole numbers.

$0.4 \times 5 = 2.0$ $3 \times 1.32 = 3.96$ $12 \times 1.2 = 14.4$

The same applies to division.

$0.4 \div 2 = 0.2$ $1.5 \div 3 = 0.5$ $13.2 \div 11 = 1.2$

> Can you see how the decimal point is used in the decimal calculations?

1. Put two crosses on the number line. One to show the point that is 0.15 **more** than 0.76, and the other to show 0.45 **less** than 0.76

   0   0.76   1

2. Arrange these numbers from largest to smallest: 0.076, 0.76, 0.7, 0.706.

   ☐　☐　☐　☐

3. The same number will make each calculation correct. Write it in the box.

   1.1 − ☐ = 0.56

   0.02 + ☐ = 0.56

4. Beth makes and sells cup cakes for charity. She makes 40 cakes and sells them all for £0.85 each. How much money will she raise altogether?

   £ ☐

5. A pizza weighs 0.6kg. It is divided into five equal slices.

   How much will each slice weigh?

   ☐ kg

6. Handwriting pens cost £1.45 each, and rulers cost £0.75 each. A teacher has to buy 30 of each, and has been given £50 by the headteacher. How much more money does she need to buy all the pens and rulers?

   Show your method.

   £ ☐

27

12 Ratio and proportion

↻ Recap

Proportion is a fraction of a whole.

For these counters, the proportion of blue counters is one in four, or one out of four.

> We can also say that the proportion of white counters is three out of four.

Ratio is different. It compares each amount.

The ratio of blue to white is 1:3.

> We can also say that the ratio of white to blue is 3:1.

📄 Learn

Proportion has a lot in common with **fractions** and **percentages**.

For the counters above $\frac{1}{4}$ or 25% are blue.

> And $\frac{3}{4}$ or 75% are white.

Scale is similar to ratio.

Maps are drawn to a scale, and accurate models are made to scale. A map scale of 1:500 means 1cm on the map equals 500cm, or 5m in real life.

A model scale of 1:10 works in the same way.

> If a cat measures 50cm in height, a model of the cat would be 5cm in height.

Ratio and proportion can be used to represent larger quantities.

The proportion of girls in a school is 3 in 5. This means three out of every five children are girls.

> So, if there are 200 children in the school, we work out the number of girls by calculating $\frac{3}{5}$ × 200.

$\frac{3}{5}$ × 200 = $\frac{600}{5}$, and 600 divided by 5 = 120 girls.

So this also tells us there must be 80 boys because 200 − 120 = 80.

Can you see the ratio of girls to boys? It is 3:2 – for every 3 girls there are 2 boys.

> Or, the ratio of boys to girls is 2:3.

1. Here are some blue and white counters.

   Complete the sentence.

   2 in every [   ] counters are blue.

2. There are 50 sheep in a field. 20 of them have black wool, the rest have white wool.

   Tick each statement that is true.

   [   ] One in three sheep have black wool.

   [   ] The ratio of white to black sheep is 3:2.

   [   ] 40% of the sheep have black wool.

3. A scale model of a house is 9cm wide and 15cm high.

   The actual house is 6m wide. How high is it?

   [   ] m

4. A vegetarian recipe states that the ratio of onions to carrots is 1 to 3, and the ratio of carrots to potatoes is 1 to 2. Jim says, "For every onion there should be 5 potatoes." Explain his mistake.

   _____

   _____

5. On a map, 1cm represents 25km. Two towns are 150km apart.

   What is the distance between them on the map?

   [   ] cm

6. In a group of 200 people, the ratio of adults to children is 3:2.

   How many children and adults are there?

   Show your method.

   [   ] children and [   ] adults

29

13 Patterns, sequences and algebra

↻ Recap

Patterns can be made with shapes using simple rules.

Number patterns can be made using rules.

For example, a 'double the number' rule gives us the sequence:

1, 2, 4, 8, 16, 32, 64, 128, and on and on forever…

It is sometimes more difficult to spot the rule.

10, 12, 15, 19 …

In this sequence the difference between the numbers changes each time. The rule is not clear. Look at the first three differences: the first is +2, then +3, then +4 and so on.

> So the next two numbers are 24 and 30. What number comes after that?

📄 Learn

In algebra we use letters instead of numbers, usually in a formula. Then, by putting a number into the place of one letter, we can find a value for the other letter.

In the formula $a = 2b$, $2b$ means 2 times b.

Notice that we don't use a multiplication sign between a letter and a number.

So, if $b = 3$ we can see that $a = 2 \times 3 = 6$.

Formulas are used all the time in daily life.

Need to convert gallons to pints? Use the formula $p = 8g$

Need to approximately convert inches to centimetres? Use the formula $c = 2.5i$

> So, for example, 3 gallons = 24 pints and 6 inches = 15cm

Some formulas can have lots of different values for each letter. For example, in $2m + n = 10$, we can try m equal to 0, 1, 2, 3, 4 and so on, and then make the formula correct by adjusting n each time.

> When $m = 0$, $n = 10$, when $m = 3$, $n = 4$

1. Use the information in the first line to fill in the box. All values are whole numbers.

    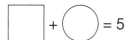 +  = 5   and $\square$ − $\bigcirc$ = 1

    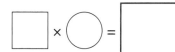 × $\bigcirc$ = $\boxed{}$

2. The rule for this sequence is multiply by 3 then take away 1.

    Write the next two numbers.

    $\qquad$ 1 $\qquad$ 2 $\qquad$ 5 $\qquad$ 14 $\qquad$ $\square$ $\quad$ $\square$

3. Explain the rule for this sequence and write what the next number will be

    $\qquad$ $1\frac{1}{2}$ $\qquad$ $2\frac{3}{4}$ $\qquad$ 4 $\qquad$ $5\frac{1}{4}$ $\qquad$ $6\frac{1}{2}$ $\qquad$ $\boxed{}$

    _____

4. Complete the table for the formula $y = 2x - 5$.

x	1			7
y		1	5	

5. Wendy creates patterns and gives them values.

    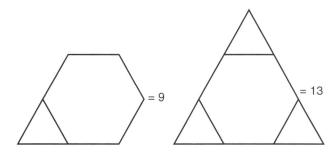

    Calculate the value of each shape.

    Triangle = $\square$ $\qquad$ Hexagon = $\square$

6. A bookseller buys second-hand books, then sells them for a profit.

    He uses a formula to calculate the selling price. He buys one book for £2 and sells it for £5, and another for £3 and sells it for £7.50.

    If he buys a book for £6, how much will he sell it for?

    £ $\boxed{}$

14 Measurement: perimeter, area and volume

↻ Recap

Perimeter is the distance around the edge of a shape. It is measured in units of length, such as centimetres or metres.

Area is the total surface of a 2D shape. It is measured in squared units, such as cm² or m².

Volume is the space a 3D shape fills. It is measured in cubed units, such as cm³ or m³.

📄 Learn

To find the perimeter of a shape add the length of each side together.

For the rectangle the perimeter is $a + a + b + b$, or $2a + 2b$.

> The formula is $P = 2a + 2b$

So, if a = 5cm and b = 7cm, the perimeter is 24cm.

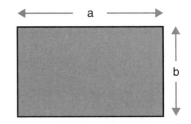

To find the area of a rectangle or square, multiply length by width.

For the rectangle shown, the area is a times b, or ab.

> The formula is $A = lw$.

So, if a = 5cm and b = 7cm, the area is 35cm².

To find the volume of a cube or cuboid, multiply the length, width and height. $V = lwh$.

So, if p = 6cm, q = 4cm, and r = 3cm, what is the volume?

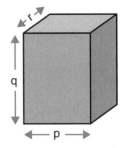

We can calculate perimeters and areas of unusual shapes. For the area, calculate the larger rectangle and then take away the area of the cut-out part.

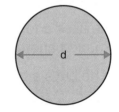

The radius is half the distance across; the diameter is the full distance across the middle: $d = 2r$.

Practice

1. A rectangle has an area of 12m². Tick each pair of side measurements that the rectangle could have.

☐ 2m, 6m   ☐ 3m, 5m   ☐ 4m, 3m   ☐ 12m, 1m

2. A park has a rectangular path around it. The park is 85m long and the width is 40m.

   Katie walks around the path until she has walked 1km. How many laps has she done? Circle the correct answer.

   2 laps   4 laps   6 laps   8 laps   10 laps

3. A school orders a new fence to be put around its wildlife area. How many metres of fence will be needed?

   [_____] m

   8 m, 20 m, 15 m

4. Josiah has five identical rectangular tiles. He places them side-by-side and says the area they cover is 30cm², and the perimeter they make is 26cm. What size is each tile?

   [_____] cm long and [_____] cm wide

5. A white circle fits exactly on top of a blue square.

   If the circle has a radius of 5cm and an area of 77.3cm², what area of the square can you still see?

   [_____] cm²

6. A cube has exactly the same volume as the cuboid shown. What is the length of each side of the cube?

   [_____] cm

   3 cm, 6 cm, 12 cm

33

15 Measurement: length, mass and capacity

↺ Recap

Length is a measure of how long things are.

We measure length in millimetres, centimetres, metres, and kilometres

> 10mm = 1cm, 100cm = 1m, 1000m = 1km

Mass is a measure of how heavy things are.

We measure mass in grams and kilograms.

> 1000g = 1kg (the word kilo means 1000).

Capacity is a measure of the volume of things, or how much they hold.

We measure capacity in millilitres, centilitres and litres.

> 10ml = 1cl,   100cl = 1l,   or 1000ml = 1l

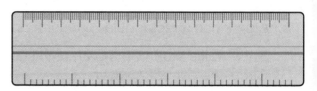

🗐 Learn

We can solve problems using measures, and do calculations just like we would with other numbers.

> 6 × 25cl = 150cl, 300g ÷ 6 = 50g, 300m × 12 = 3600m (or 3.6km)

Remember, for some calculations we may have to convert units, and converting between metric units always requires multiplying or dividing by a power of 10. For example, to add 1 litre to 500ml, we can do two things:

1 litre = 1000ml, so 1000 + 500 = 1500ml. Or, 500ml = 0.5l, so 1 + 0.5 = 1.5l

> This also tells us that 1500ml = 1.5l

To convert grams to kilograms, divide by 1000. To convert kilograms to grams, multiply by 1000.

> For 1.5kg + 300g, 1500 + 300g = 1800g or 1.8kg

To convert metres to kilometres, divide by 1000. To convert kilometres to metres, multiply by 1000.

> For 2km – 450m, 2 – 0.45 = 1.55km or 1550m

1. Lisa lists some animals, and estimates their mass from lightest to heaviest.

   Draw lines to match each animal to its estimated mass.

Hamster	Cat	Horse	Elephant

3200kg	3.6kg	0.032kg	360kg

2. Ralph has a pencil 12.7cm long. He sharpens it once a day, and each time the pencil loses 5mm of its length. How long will it be after five days?

   [   ] cm

3. Hanmo has a 0.75 litre bottle of lemonade. If she fills a 320ml jug, how much lemonade will still be in the bottle?

   Give your answer in litres or millimetres.

   [   ] l or [   ] ml

4. Jim wants to convert miles into kilometres. He knows that 5 miles equals 8 kilometres, and then calculates that 30 miles equals 48km.

   Explain his method.

   _____

   _____

5. Dave's dad is potting plants. He has a bag of soil that weighs 5kg, and puts 225g into each of 11 identical pots.

   How much soil will he have left over? Give your answer in kilograms or grams.

   Show your method.

   [   ] kg

6. A machine in a paint factory makes 250ml of paint every second. How many litres will it make in one hour?

   [   ] litres

16 Geometry: angles and shapes

↻ Recap

Straight lines can be parallel, perpendicular, or they can meet at an angle.

Just as we can measure lines in cm, we can measure angles too. We measure them in **degrees**.

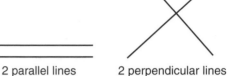
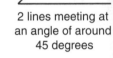

2 parallel lines   2 perpendicular lines   2 lines meeting at an angle of around 45 degrees

2D shapes are made from straight lines and angles (apart from circles).

Equilateral triangle   Rectangle   Regular pentagon   Regular hexagon   Circle

📋 Learn

A complete turn is 360°, the same as four right angles: $4 \times 90° = 360°$.

The angles in a triangle always add up to 180°.

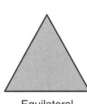  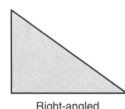 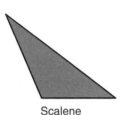

Equilateral   Isosceles   Right-angled   Scalene

The angles of quadrilaterals always add up to 360°

   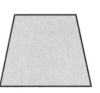 

Square   Rectangle   Rhombus   Parallelogram   Trapezium   Kite

3D shapes are made by connecting 2D shapes along their edges.

Cube   Cuboid   Cone   Sphere   Cylinder   Triangular prism   Square-based pyramid

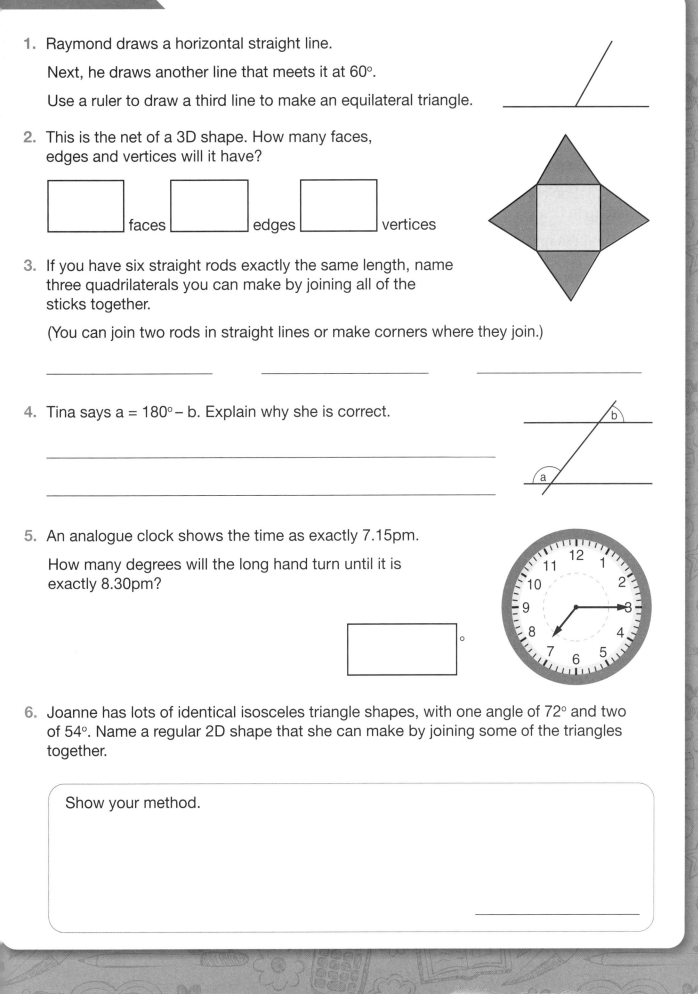

Practice

1. Raymond draws a horizontal straight line.

   Next, he draws another line that meets it at 60°.

   Use a ruler to draw a third line to make an equilateral triangle.

2. This is the net of a 3D shape. How many faces, edges and vertices will it have?

   [   ] faces [   ] edges [   ] vertices

3. If you have six straight rods exactly the same length, name three quadrilaterals you can make by joining all of the sticks together.

   (You can join two rods in straight lines or make corners where they join.)

   _____   _____   _____

4. Tina says a = 180° – b. Explain why she is correct.

   _____

   _____

5. An analogue clock shows the time as exactly 7.15pm.

   How many degrees will the long hand turn until it is exactly 8.30pm?

   [   ] °

6. Joanne has lots of identical isosceles triangle shapes, with one angle of 72° and two of 54°. Name a regular 2D shape that she can make by joining some of the triangles together.

   Show your method.

   _____

37

17 Geometry: position, direction and coordinates

↻ Recap

A coordinate grid has an x-axis and a y-axis.

We can plot points on the grid, and we always write the x-coordinate first.

Point D on the grid has coordinates (2, 4).

> Find the coordinates for E and F.

We can join points together to make shapes.

> What shape could you make if you joined D to F, then F to E?

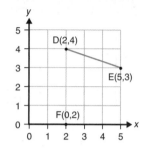

Remember: along the corridor then up the stairs!

📄 Learn

We can also have negative coordinates.

Point G on the grid has the coordinates (−3, 2).

> Find the coordinates for H.

We can **reflect** points, lines and shapes in mirror lines.

> So if the y-axis was a mirror line, the reflection of G would be (3, 2) and H would be (2, −4). Can you see where the reflected line would be?

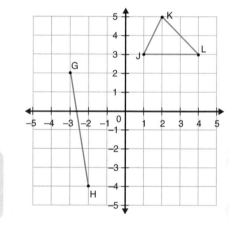

We can also **translate** points, lines and shapes.

We write a translation the same as coordinates.

> If the shape JKL was translated by (1, −2) it would be moved 1 to the right and 2 down.

> So, in the translated triangle, point J would move to (2, 1). Can you see where K and L would move to?

Don't forget, in reflections the line or shape is moved and reversed. In translation it is just moved, but the translated shape has stayed the same.

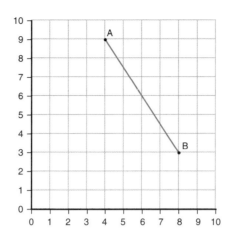

1. There is a straight line drawn from A to B on the graph.

   Write the coordinates for its halfway point.

   (____ , ____)

2. Point C is a point on the graph. When it is joined to A and B it makes a right-angled triangle. Circle the correct coordinates for C.

   (8, 4)   (4, 8)   (8, 9)   (9, 3)   (9, 8)

3. Jeremy says, "If the line is translated so that point A moves to (2, 6), then the new co-ordinates for B will be (6, 6)."

   Explain his mistake.

   _____

   _____

4. Ella draws a line from one of the corners to the point (5, 0). The line crosses the y-axis at (0, 1). Circle the corner she drew the line from.

   P   Q   R   S

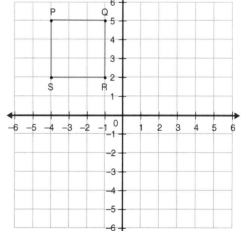

5. The square PQRS is reflected in the x-axis. Draw the new shape on the coordinate grid, and write the letter T next to P's reflection.

6. Tim draws a line, (3, −4) to (3, 2). It is the first line of a rectangle. That will have the y-axis as a line of symmetry. Write the coordinates of the other two corners.

   (____ , ____) and (____ , ____)

18 Time, distance and speed

We measure and calculate time in a different way from other measures.

There are 60 seconds in one minute; 60 minutes in one hour; 24 hours in one day; seven days in one week; 28, 29, 30 or 31 days in one month; 365 days in a year; and 366 days in a leap year, which occurs once every four years.

Time can be shown on 12- or 24-hour clocks. 6pm is 18:00.

> We often use 24-hour digital times in timetables.

Distance is measured in metres and kilometres.

(And sometimes small distances are measured in centimetres and millimetres.)

1km = 1000m, 1m = 100cm, 1cm = 10mm

🗐 Learn

Speed measures how fast something is travelling.

> A car might travel at 50km per hour, and a person might walk at 3km per hour.

Speed is distance divided by time.

> If a motorbike travels 90km in three hours, its speed will be 30km per hour. We can write this as 30kph or km/h.

If a boy walks at 3kph for two hours, how far will he walk?

> If he walks 3km each hour, then he must have walked 6km after two hours.

Sometimes, distance and time are shown on a graph, with time on the x-axis.

Beth walked to town to see her friend Ashton. The graph shows her distance from home. At 12 noon she is at home.

She walks 4km in two hours. Then sits in the park for one and a half hours. She then walks home in two hours.

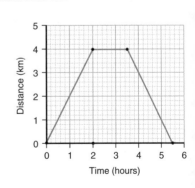

> The graph is flat at the top because she is sitting down.

1. The timetable shows bus times to Ruby's school.

Departs Bus Stop	07:05	07:20	07:35	07:50	08:05
Arrives School	07:50	08:05	08:20	08:35	08:50

If Ruby has to be at school before 8.30am, which is the latest bus that she could catch? Circle the departure time on the timetable.

2. Fill in the boxes.

3 years = ☐ months   eight weeks = ☐ days   five days = ☐ hours

3. In a non-leap year, which three months have the most days? Circle the correct answer.

        January, February, March   July, August, September

How many more days do those three months have?

☐ more days.

4. The graph shows the journey of a lorry between two cities. Kevin says, "The driver stopped for 90 minutes." Explain why he is correct.

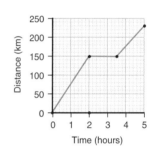

_____

_____

5. How fast was the lorry travelling for the first part of the journey?

☐ kph

6. The distance from a house to a beach is 20km. Holly leaves the house at 9am, walking at 4kph. Isabelle leaves the house two hours later on a bicycle, travelling at 8kph. If neither of them stop, who will arrive first, and by how much time?

Show your method.

_____ will arrive first by ☐ hours and ☐ minutes

19 Data handling: simple charts

A collection of information and numbers is known as data. This table shows the number of sandwich lunches asked for by Class 4 each day of the week.

Day	Monday	Tuesday	Wednesday	Thursday	Friday
Sandwiches	7	8	10	4	9

This data can be represented in different ways.

Tally chart

Day	Sandwiches
Mon	ⵑⵑⵑⵑⵑ ||
Tue	ⵑⵑⵑⵑⵑ |||
Wed	ⵑⵑⵑⵑⵑ ⵑⵑⵑⵑⵑ
Thu	||||
Fri	ⵑⵑⵑⵑⵑ ||||

Pictogram

Bar chart

📄 Learn

Pictograms can also use one icon to represent two or more objects, and bar charts can have different scales. Now, one sandwich icon is used for every two sandwiches eaten. And the scale on the bar chart is one square for two.

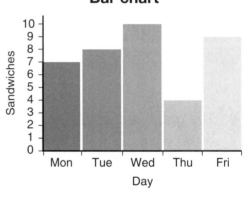

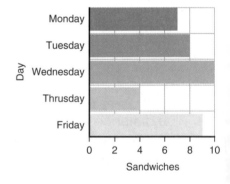

Which day were the most sandwiches made? **Wednesday**

How many more sandwiches were made on Tuesday than Thursday? **Four more.**

How many fewer sandwiches were made on Wednesday than the rest of the week? **18**

Practice

1. A tally chart for a survey of 30 children is unfinished. Half as many children have blond hair as have black hair. Complete the chart.

Black	Blond	Brown	Red
		ⵑⵑⵑ ⵑⵑⵑ ⵑⵑⵑ ⵑⵑⵑ ⵑⵑⵑ III	III
		18	3

2. Circle the hair colour that $\frac{3}{5}$ of the children have.

        Blond   Black   Brown   Red

3. A farmer has four fields. There are some sheep in each field.

   A pictogram uses one icon to represent every two sheep in each field.

   Ian says that more than one third of the sheep are in field B.

   Explain why he is right.

Field	Sheep
Field A	🐑
Field B	🐑🐑🐑🐑
Field C	🐑🐑🐑
Field D	🐑🐑🐑

   _____

   _____

4. Four more sheep arrive. Which field should they be placed in so that the field has exactly $\frac{1}{4}$ of all the sheep?

   Field ☐

5. A bar chart shows the number of rides each day on a helter skelter at a fairground. How many more rides were there on the most popular day than on the least popular day?

   ☐ rides

6. What proportion of all the rides were taken on Tuesday?

   > Show your method.
   >
   > ☐ out of ☐

43

20 Data handling: graphs, pie charts and statistics

↻ Recap

Line graphs are useful for comparing two different measures like distance and time.

> We can use this line graph to calculate how temperature changes during the day. Remember that the temperature can be negative.

Can you see the highest and lowest temperatures?

> 3°C at 8pm, −2°C from 12pm to 1am.

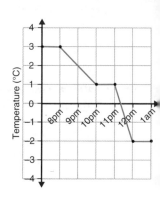

Pie charts use angles to represent proportions of amounts.

> A complete circle has 360°, so 90° will be one-quarter, 180° one-half.

> The pie chart shows us that half the food is pizzas. Notice that it doesn't tell us how many pizzas, just the proportion of them.

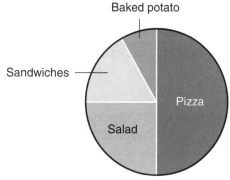

Baked potato
Sandwiches
Pizza
Salad

If we know there were 24 meals altogether, we can work out how many of each type there would be.

> Twelve pizzas, six salads, four sandwiches and two baked potatoes.

📄 Learn

Any set of data has an average, which we call the **mean**.

To find the mean, we add up each item of data, and then divide the total by how many items there are.

In a school there are 23 pupils in Class 1, 25 in Class 2, 21 in Class 3 and 19 in Class 4.

> The total number of children is: 23 + 25 + 21 + 19 = 88, so the mean class size is 88 ÷ 4 = 22.

For the temperature graph above, to find the mean temperature we add each of the temperatures then divide by seven, because there are seven different readings – one per hour.

> 3 + 3 + 2 + 1 + 1 -2 -2 = 6, then 6 ÷ 7 = 0.86°C. This is the mean temperature.

1. Leila calculates the mean for a group of six numbers to be 5.

$$2 + \boxed{} + 7 + 3 + 9 + 5$$

Circle the missing number.

3   4   5   6   7

2. What is the difference in temperature between the lowest and highest temperatures?

 °C

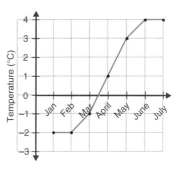

3. Joel says that the mean temperature for April to July is 4°C. Explain his mistake.

_____

_____

4. Arrange each of these digits in the number sentence to make it true.

4   5   6   9

The mean of ☐, ☐ and ☐ is ☐.

5. The pie chart shows the favourite birds of 90 people. If 20 people like wrens best and 25 like robins, what is the angle for each on the chart?

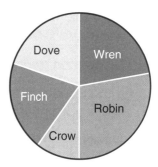

Wrens: ☐ °   Robins: ☐ °

6. If the angles for finches and doves are both 72°, how many people like crows best?

Show your method.

☐ people

1. Kerry thinks of a number. | **63,389** |

   She rounds it to the nearest thousand, and then adds ten thousand.

   What number will she have now?

2. Circle each fraction that is larger than $\frac{3}{5}$.

   $\frac{3}{4}$ $\frac{6}{10}$ $\frac{1}{2}$ $\frac{14}{20}$

3. Ollie says, "I have drawn a triangle that is both a right-angled triangle AND an isosceles triangle."

   Explain why he could be correct.

   _____

   _____

   Write the size of the three angles in Ollie's triangle.

   [   ] °   [   ] °   [   ] °

4. AB is the first line of a square that is symmetrical about the x-axis.

   Draw lines to complete the square.

   If the square is translated by (3, 2), what will be the new coordinates of A and B?

   A new: (_____ , _____)   B new: (_____ , _____)

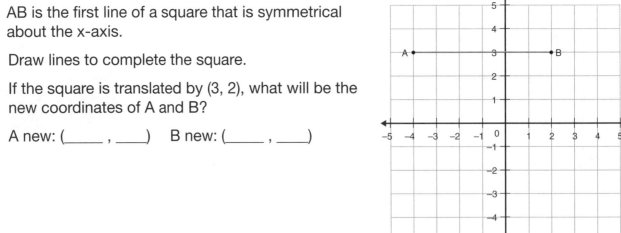

5. Use each of these digits once to complete the calculation.

1   **2**   **3**   **5**

$$\frac{\square}{\square} \div \frac{\square}{\square} = \frac{5}{6}$$

6. The bar chart shows how some children travel to school.

How many more children walk and bike in total than those who come by car?

[___] children

What percentage of the class bike to school?

[___] %

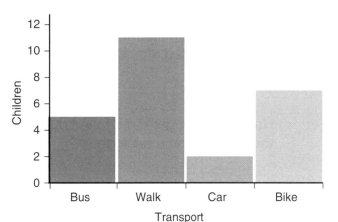

Children (y-axis: 0, 2, 4, 6, 8, 10, 12)

Bus — Walk — Car — Bike

Transport

7. Use this pattern of number pairs to complete the rule

$q = $ [___] $\times p -$ [___]

p	1	2	3	4
q	−1	1	3	5

Complete this sentence: when $p = 15$, $q = $ [___]

8. A return bus ticket to Amina's school costs £2.30. She can also buy a monthly pass for £49. If she makes 25 return trips to school in a month, how much will she save by using a monthly pass?

£ [___]

9. A factory packs apples into sacks. Sacks can hold 220 apples. If the average mass of an apple is 95g, what will a full sack weigh in kilograms?

[___] kg

10. Louise cycles up a steep hill and then back again. The graph shows her journey.

What speed did Louise cycle for the first half hour? Give your answer in kilometres per hour.

Distance (Metres) / Time (Minutes)

[   ] kph

What happened after 30 minutes?

_____

How much longer did it take Louise to reach the top from when she started, than it took her to come back down?

[   ] minutes

11. Yusef has a bag of 24 balloons. They are either red or blue.

The ratio of red to blue balloons is 5 red : 3 blue.

He takes out three red and three blue balloons. What is the new ratio of red to blue?

[   ] red: [   ] blue

12. A cube is made by joining six square tiles. If the perimeter of one tile is 20cm, calculate the area of the whole surface of the cube.

Show your method.

[   ] cm²

Calculate the volume of the cube: [   ] cm³